WILD
Animals

Come and discover the wild animals
in this fun activity book!

•

Use pens, pencils and stickers
to complete the activities on each page.

•

Where there is a missing sticker, you will see
an empty shape. Search your sticker pages
to find the missing sticker.

Don't forget to press out and play
a ROAR-some card game from
the card pages at the back of the book!

make
believe
ideas

Jolly giraffe

Colour the jolly giraffe.

Point to the parrot
flying in the sky.

Silly snake

Use a pencil to trace the path to the tree.

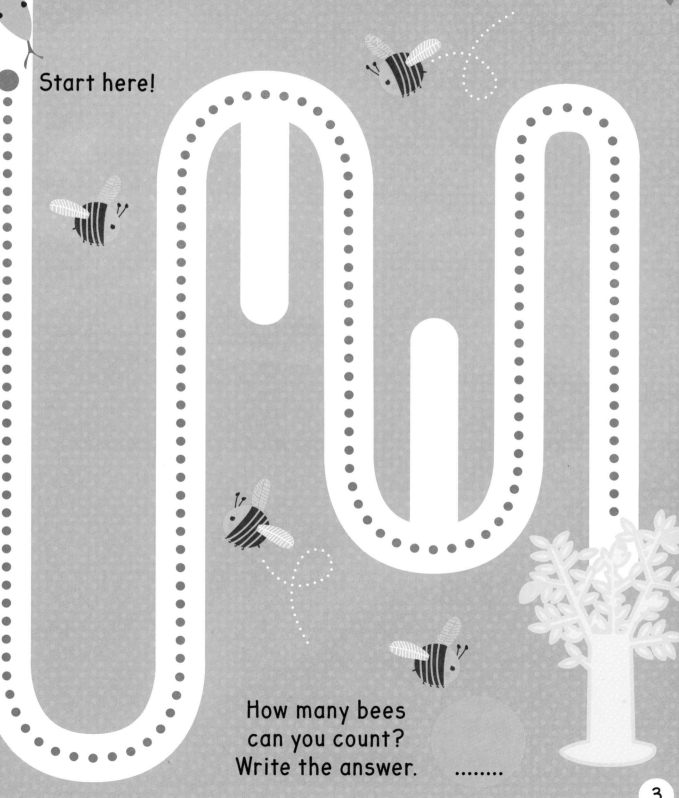

Start here!

How many bees
can you count?
Write the answer.   ....

Perfect pairs

Draw lines to match the animals.

Terrific tracks

Trace the animal tracks
with your finger.

Where is the carrot?
Trace the tick when
you've found it.

Where do I live?

Use colour and stickers to discover
where the animals live!

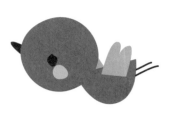

In the sky

In the mountains

In the Arctic

By the river

Monkey mischief

Find three differences between the scenes.

Sticker the star when you have finished and say, "I did it!"

Odd One Out

Circle the one that doesn't belong in each row.

Tasty treats

Follow the lines to see which
animal gets the juicy apple.

Playful penguin

Trace the penguin.
Then, colour him in.

Can you find the orange fish? Trace the tick when you've found it.

Sweet sums

Count the animals to finish the sums.

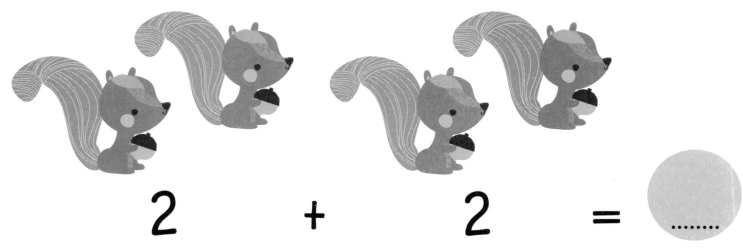

2   +   2   = ...

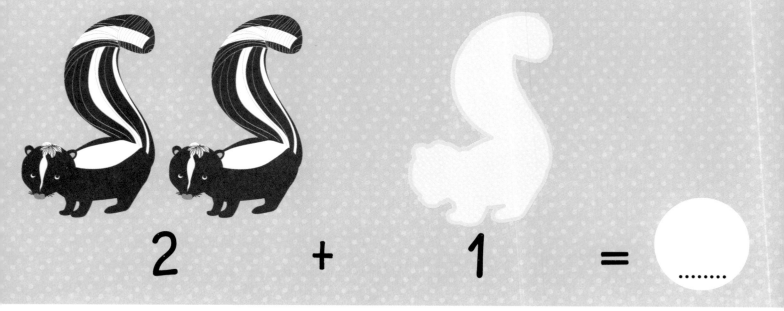

2   +   1   = ...

2   +   3   = ...

fantastic fox

Join the dots to finish the tail.
Then, count to five.

3
5
1
4
2

Sticker a purple flower to finish the pattern.

Colouring fun

Colour the
bird purple.

Colour the
bear orange.

Sticker the
blue baby hippo.

Colour the
butterflies yellow.

In the sea

How many of each sea creature can you count?
Write the answers in the spaces below.

....

dolphin   fish   octopus

Sleepy snail

Colour the sleepy snail. Use the coloured dots as a guide.

Memory match

1 Press out the cards and place them facedown on the table.

2 Turn over two cards at a time. If they match, put them to one side. If they don't, turn them over and try again.

3 Keep going until you've found all the pairs!

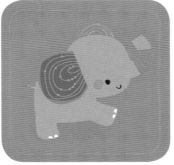

Stickers for pages 2–3

Pages 4–5

Pages 6–7

Pages 8–9

Pages 8–9 continued

Pages 10–11

I did it!

Pages 12–13

Pages 14–15

Page 16